Published in the UK by
POWERFRESH Limited
3 Gray Street
Northampton
NN1 3QQ

Telephone 01604 630 996
Facsimile 01604 621 013
E Mail   pwrfresh@nccnet.co.uk

GW00858365

Cover and interior layout by Powerfresh

ISBN 1 874125 775

Printed in the UK by Avalon Print Northampton
Powerfresh September 1998

Piggery Jokery

THE SILVEY - JEX PARTNERSHIP

WHY IS IT ALWAYS _YOU_ THAT GOES WEE-WEE ALL THE WAY HOME?

OOH... A SILK PURSE
AND YOU MADE IT YOURSELVES
...OUT OF.. GULP!!
HAPPY BIRTHDAY MUM XX
SJ.

MUST YOU SMOKE IN THE LOO - YOU'LL STINK THE PLACE OUT

THE PIG & WHISTLE

BACK EVERYONE ..... HERE HE COMES

A TROUGH FOR TWO PLEASE

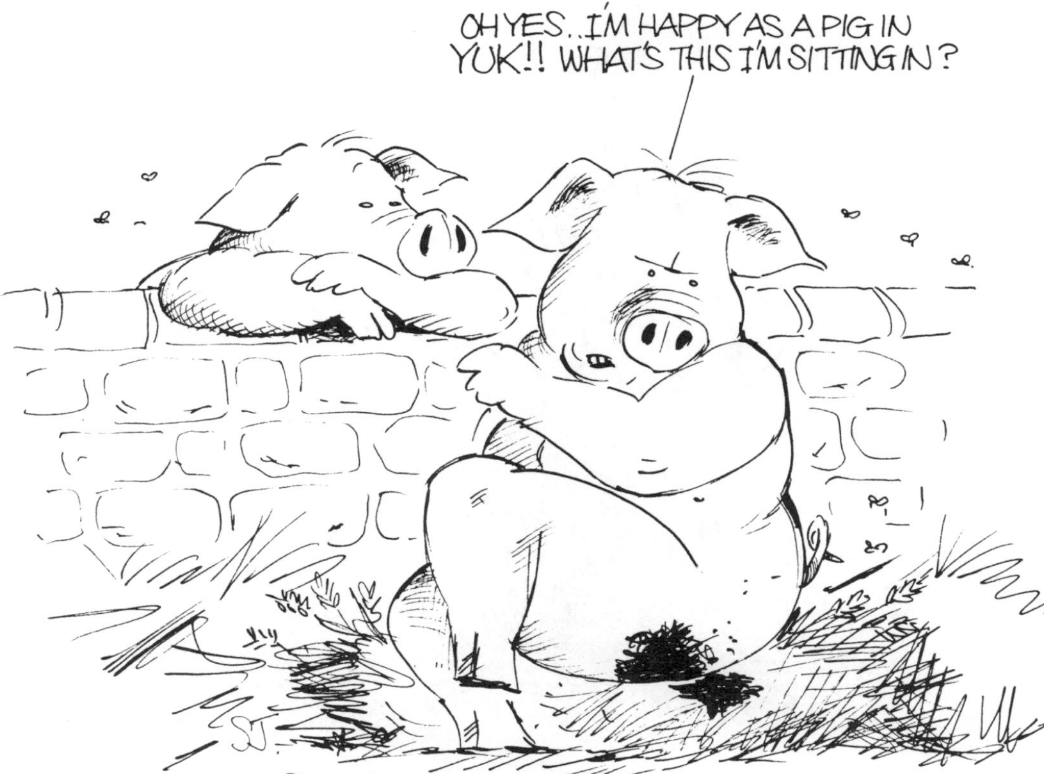
OH YES...I'M HAPPY AS A PIG IN
YUK!! WHAT'S THIS I'M SITTING IN?
SJ

THAT BLOODY PIG TREATS THIS PLACE LIKE A HOME FROM HOME

WHAT'S THAT OLD SAYING-"ONE DAY PIGS MIGHT"...SOMETHING OR OTHER?

OKAY CHAPS HERE'S THE PLAN...WHEN THE FARMER COMES IN WITH THE SWILL
CHALKY STANDS ON THE BOX AND CLAMPS THE BUCKET OVER THE BLIGHTERS HEAD
WE OVERPOWER HIM, TIE HIM UP WITH THIS ROPE & GINGER GRABS THE KEYS TO THE TOOL SHED
THEN ARMED WITH PITCHFORKS WE STORM THE PERIMETER FENCE, STOP THE BUS TO ICKLESHAM
AND FORCE THE DRIVER TO TAKE US TO THE WOODS THE OTHER SIDE OF TOWN...AND FREEDOM!
WHAT DO YOU THINK?

TITLES BY
POWERFRESH
· NORTHAMPTON · ENGLAND ·

CRINKLED 'N' WRINKLED

DRIVEN CRAZY

TRUE LOVE

IT'S A BOY

IT'S A GIRL

OH NO IT'S XMAS AGAIN

FUNNY SIDE OF 30s

FUNNY SIDE OF 40 HIM

FUNNY SIDE OF 40 HER

FUNNY SIDE OF 50 HIM

FUNNY SIDE OF 50 HER

FUNNY SIDE OF 60'S

FUNNY SIDE OF SEX

FLYING FUNNIES

GOLFAHOLICS

CHUNKY "N HUNKY

FOOTNOTES

MIDLIFE CRISIS

WE'RE GETTING MARRIED

THE DEFINITIVE GUIDE TO VASECTOMY

KEEP FIT WITH YOUR CAT

MARITAL BLISS AND OTHER OXYMORONS

THE OFFICE FROM HELL

PMT CRAZED

HORNY MAN'S ADULT DOODLE BOOK

HORNY GIRL'S ADULT DOODLE BOOK

IF BABIES COULD TALK

CAT CRAZY

MAD TO TRAVEL BY AIR...

MAD TO PLAY GOLF...

MAD TO HAVE A BABY...

MAD TO GET MARRIED...

MAD TO HAVE A PONY

MAD TO HAVE A CAT

MAD TO HAVE A COMPUTER

YOU DON'T HAVE TO BE MAD TO BE 40 HIM

YOU DON'T HAVE TO BE MAD TO BE 40 HER

YOU DON'T HAVE TO BE MAD TO BE 50 HIM

YOU DON'T HAVE TO BE MAD TO BE 50 HER

MAD ON FOOTBALL

MAD TO BE A MOTHER

MAD TO BE A FATHER

THE BARE BOTTOM BOOK

GOOD WHILE IT LASTED

FUNNY FARM SILLY MOOS

FUNNY FARM PIGGERY JOKERY

For more information on these or other titles please write to :
Powerfresh Ltd. 3 Gray Street, Northampton, NN1 3QQ, ENGLAND.
Telephone 01604 630 996 Fax 01604 621 013
E Mail pwrfresh@ nccnet.co.uk